Performance Series

WP193

MW00669067

Romantic Piano Duets

for one piano, four hands

edited by Weekley and Arganbright

Kjos **Neil A. Kjos Music Company** • San Diego, California

About the Editors

Dallas Weekley and **Nancy Arganbright** are unique because they have concentrated their performances and research almost entirely on the duet literature. Their research has resulted in the discovery and the revival of a number of important one piano, four-hand works, several of which have been published.

Through their concerts in the United States and abroad, recordings, publications, research, workshops, and the annual Four-Hand Fest in La Crosse, they have dedicated themselves to popularizing the four-hand medium.

Weekley and Arganbright are faculty members at the University of Wisconsin, La Crosse. Their home, which is included in the National Register of Historic Homes, has received much of their extra-curricular attention for restoration work.

For other fine editions and sparkling arrangements by Weekley and Arganbright, please see the back cover.

Dedicated to Walter Robert — pianist, scholar, our beloved teacher.

Contents

ISBN 0-8497-9385-8

Venetian Boat Song

Felix Mendelssohn
completed by Weekley & Arganbright

Measures 1-20 were written by Mendelssohn. Weekley and Arganbright completed the work based on Mendelssohn's fragments. The title was given by the editors.

WP193

*To turn the page, it may work for the primo partner to play all the notes with one hand and turn with the other.

Song Without Words
opus 30 number 1

Felix Mendelssohn
arranged by Carl Czerny

Nocturne
Number 5

John Field
arranged by Franz Liszt

In order to make the page turns more convenient in "Bagatelle," this page is intentionally blank.

Bagatelle
opus 47 number 1

Antonin Dvořák